ONE HUNDRE[...]
in
ENGLISH USAGE
and
COMPOSITION

By

T.H. DALZELL, M.A., H.Dip. Ed.

BOOK III

© T.H. DALZELL, 1983.

ISBN 0 7169 4017 5

A CENTURY SERIES

ROBERT GIBSON & SONS, GLASGOW, LTD.,
17 FITZROY PLACE, GLASGOW G3 7SF.

ISBN 0 7169 4017 5

PREFACE

THIS book, intended for the English study of ten-year-olds in Primary and Preparatory schools, contains a variety of exercises which have proved their usefulness.

The aims of this book are:—

(1) To supplement the teacher's own work in language training.

(2) To help to eliminate common errors of speech and writing.

(3) To enable the pupil to write lucid, properly-punctuated sentences.

(4) To enlarge the pupil's vocabulary.

(5) To provide exercises in paragraphing.

(6) To suggest suitable topics for oral and written exercises in composition.

The book should prove a valuable time-saver for the busy teacher and, in addition, allow the pupil to undertake the work for the maximum time during the English period.

The synopsis at the beginning of the book will assist the teacher to use it to the best advantage in conjunction with his own scheme of work.

T. H. D.

Printed by Bell and Bain Ltd., Glasgow

SYNOPSIS

SYNOPSIS *(Continued)*

EXERCISE 1

Some of the following are sentences.   Write out the sentences:

1. Running and jumping.
2. This is no way to do it.
3. I'll be there.
4. On and on they came.
5. Those big, juicy pears.
6. Away on yonder hill.
7. In rushed Jimmy.
8. As he walked down the street.

EXERCISE 2

Re-write the following, putting in capital letters, apostrophes and punctuation marks:

1. john the pipers son stole a pig and away he ran
2. prince charles and princess diana went holidaying in scotland
3. my sister mary is sailing on the queen elizabeth to america next sunday
4. its a days journey from belfast to cork
5. father mother jill and i spent christmas with uncle john and aunt susan and they have promised to spend easter with us
6. cousin jack and i visited the lakes of killarney on august bank holiday

EXERCISE 3

Look at the pairs of words given below.   If the two words have nearly the same meaning, write " S " after them; if they are opposite in meaning write " O " after them.

1. valuable, worthless.
2. abode, dwelling.
3. supply, demand.
4. sense, nonsense.

5. first, foremost.
6. gain, benefit.
7. servant, master.
8. question, query.

EXERCISE 4

Re-arrange the following groups of words to read sensibly:
1. The fruit like she to cut not did
2. For dinner neither of us much had appetite
3. The table round us all arranged mother me to place opposite taking care her
4. Well-liked in the town, a very clean, honest man, the lame shoemaker was
5. Cheered spectators the players over and again over the
6. Of goat-skin made a cap great high shapeless wore Crusoe

EXERCISE 5

Combine each of the following pairs of sentences into one sentence using " and " or " but ":
1. It was very dark.   I could see the path.
2. The night was foggy.   The bus was late.
3. John is a little fellow.   He is fairly strong.
4. They spoke in a whisper.   I heard their plans.
5. The boys played very hard.   They won the game.
6. My father drove fast.   He managed to catch the boat.

EXERCISE 6

Combine each of the following pairs of sentences into one sentence using " who," " whose," " which " or " that ":

Example: James repaired the roof. It had been damaged by the storm.
James repaired the roof which had been damaged by the storm.

1. I saw the beggar. He had once been wealthy.
2. The book is in our library. It is very exciting.
3. Shirley went to visit her uncle. He is a farmer.
4. That old lady is my grandmother. Her house was burgled.
5. Dick drove the car to town. He is a good driver.
6. I saw the jet fighter. It flew over our village.
7. Bill was the captain of the school team. He was the tallest boy.
8. I caught the ball. It was driven towards me.

EXERCISE 7

Complete the following sentences to ask questions:
1. Could you ....
2. Why did the ....
3. Where are ....
4. Have the boys ....
5. Who said ....
6. Which road ....
7. When ....
8. How ....

EXERCISE 8

Fill in the blanks with " were " or " where ":
1. .... you at the concert?
2. I wonder .... Jim has gone?
3. We .... going to the woods .... we could gather wild flowers.

4. .... you going so late last night?
5. We .... looking for a place .... we might
camp for the night.
6. .... they .... standing was once the scene
of a terrible fight.

EXERCISE 9

**"Isn't " is the shorter form of " is not." Write the
following in their shorter forms:**
1. It is.
2. Cannot.
3. I will.
4. There is.
5. Could not.
6. Will not.
7. I would.
8. Would not.

EXERCISE 10

**Re-write the following sentences, putting in words
of <u>opposite</u> meaning to those in italics:**
1. Jack *bought* some *sour* apples.
2. He *found* his tools *inside* the house.
3. The *boy* taught *his sister* to play tennis.
4. *He* did *his* work *quickly* and *quietly*.
5. During the *day* there was a *light* shower of rain.
6. The *man* walked *slowly* and *carefully* through the room.

EXERCISE 11

Combine the following pairs of sentences:
1. Fred played football.   I played football.
2. You must work hard.   Mary must work hard.

3. He saw the accident.   I saw the accident.
4. The bull chased Nell.   The bull chased me.
5. The race thrilled me.   The race thrilled Jimmy.
6. I was pleased to see the match.   My brother was pleased to see the match.

EXERCISE 12

Re-write the following sentences, leaving out what is unnecessary:

1. He arrived at his work at 8 a.m. this morning.
2. Tom he is going to the cinema to-day.
3. Mina went to the shop for to buy a new coat.
4. He had got a thousand stamps in his album.
5. That is too big of a load for a little girl to carry.
6. Every day we do reading, and writing and arithmetic.
7. We leave school at 3.30 p.m. in the afternoon.
8. The man has not done nothing all day.

EXERCISE 13

1. Someone asks you what you would like to be when you grow up.   What is your reply?
2. Father has given you a present on your birthday. What do you say in returning thanks for the gift?
3. You are sent to the grocer's for a kilogramme jar of marmalade and a packet of bacon.   What do you say to the assistant?
4. You have a punctured tyre on your bicycle. What do you say to the man at the cycle shop?
5. You are late for school through no fault of your own. Explain to your teacher why you are not on time?
6. Playing in the school grounds you have accidentally broken a classroom window.   Explain to your teacher how it happened.

EXERCISE 14

What are the shortened forms or abbreviations for the following?

1. Doctor ....
2. County ....
3. Street ....
4. Monday ....
5. February ....
6. metre
     (length) ....
7. litre ....
8. minute ....
9. gramme (weight) ....
10. Mister ....
11. James ....
12. Road ....
13. Christmas ....
14. September ....
15. centimetre
      (length) ....
16. knight ....
17. mathematics ....
18. second (time) ....

EXERCISE 15

Which word in each group does not fit in with the others?

1. house, home, school, residence, dwelling.
2. speedy, fast, early, rapid, quick.
3. bent, old, aged, elderly, ancient.
4. tiny, hole, small, little, wee.
5. cost, price, value, size, expense.
6. big, huge, large, enormous, square.
7. speak, listen, talk, tell, say.
8. courageous, daring, bold, powerful, fearless.
9. master, pupil, scholar, student, learner.
10. dull, dark, deadly, dusky, dim.

EXERCISE 16

Fill in the spaces with words taken from the brackets:

1. The cat ran .... with a piece .... fish.
   (of, off.)

2. She .... she could put the thread .... the eye of the needle .... she knew it was very tiny. (through, thought, though.)
3. It was .... certain that he had been very .... and .... in his actions. (quiet, quick, quite.)
4. Have you .... heard of the girl who .... made an error but who did .... exercise in a .... careful way? (ever, every, very, never.)
5. He should .... given you .... the parcels to carry. (half, of, have.)
6. That nut is ....; you will .... it if you are not careful. (lose, loose.)

EXERCISE 17

In the following sentences place quotation marks round the actual words of the speaker; use commas to separate the spoken words from the rest of the sentence; make capitals where necessary and put in full stops or question marks:

1. I am going to the Show to-morrow said nell
2. Where are you going jack asked his mother
3. How do you expect to find the trail in this thick forest said the old man
4. I am going to find the treasure remarked John
5. Come here William said the teacher and I ll show you what to do
6. Shall i go with you suggested jane to the old lady
7. On returning mother said i am very pleased to see that you have prepared tea
8. Said the van-man could you help me bob to lift this box on to the van please

11

EXERCISE 18

Combine the following pairs of sentences using "when," "until," "as" or "after":

1. We played football. The rain was over.
2. Harry waited at the gate. I came out to play.
3. I was going to the market. I saw a car accident.
4. Polly calls for his food. We sit down to tea.
5. We watched the strange aircraft. We could see it no longer.
6. They enjoyed a delightful tea. They had games and guessing competitions.

EXERCISE 19

Fill in the blank spaces with the correct word taken from the brackets:

1. The five brushes in that box (is, are) mine.
2. (Were, was) you at the theatre last night?
3. What would you do if you (was, were) I?
4. What (is, are) the title of the book you mentioned?
5. This box of instruments (were, was) on sale at fifty pence.
6. There (is, are) some of our team.
7. What (was, were) you doing on Saturday afternoon?

EXERCISE 20

Combine each of the following pairs of sentences using "where," "when," "while," "as," "although" and "since":

1. I was walking through the woods. I heard a shrill scream.
2. He reached his destination. He was met by his two friends.

12

3. We were climbing slowly up the steep path. We were startled by a falling rock.
4. She was playing.   We were working.
5. John is a good swimmer.   He was nearly drowned.
6. There had been no rain for weeks.   The water supply was low.

EXERCISE 21

Complete the following sentences:
1. Harry did his best but ....
2. She crossed the road without first looking both ways and ....
3. As the bus was late ....
4. Although the old woman was poor, ...
5. You must be on your guard or ....
6. Do not call for me unless ....

EXERCISE 22

Re-write each of the following sentences in a <u>shorter</u> form:
1. Mr. Craig painted several pictures which are very beautiful.
2. We went to a party at Pat's house and it was most enjoyable.
3. I have a good friend called John Brown.
4. The house belonging to my uncle Tom has a large orchard.
5. We returned to camp before the sun set.
6. When nurse went into the sick room she went in as quietly as a mouse would go in.

13

EXERCISE 23

In the following fill the spaces with the words that the speaker might say:

1. The soldier took careful aim and said, " ...."
2. A visitor who had gone to the Lake District said, " ...."
3. " ....," read Susan from the letter.
4. " ....," shouted the captain of the losing team.
5. When I met my old friend I said, " ...."
6. " ....," said the teacher.

EXERCISE 24

Arrange the following groups of words into a sentence:

to have a rest and watch the golden sun
after a hard day's work
sink to rest behind the blue mountains
in the fields
I sat down by the roadside
when I was returning home

EXERCISE 25

Re-write the following sentences, placing the group of words in the brackets near the word in the sentence that it describes:

Example: *The heat was very great.   (of the furnace.)*
          The heat <u>of the furnace</u> was very great.

1. The rumbling was heard in the distance. (of thunder.)
2. The noises kept us awake during the night.   (from the factory.)
3. The first news we had was in the morning papers.   (of the air crash.)

14

4. Send to the editor of the newspaper your answer. (to the Quiz.)
5. Please help us to find the girl. (who is lost.)
6. Let her know that the door is not locked. (of the bungalow.)

EXERCISE 26

Look at these two ways of saying the same thing:

The boys of Britain should be very proud of their country.
British boys should be proud of their country.

Re-write the following sentences using shorter forms of the words in italics:

1. The people *of America* are noted for their generosity.
2. The people *of Canada* speak the language *spoken in England.*
3. The people *of France* are well-mannered.
4. The wool *of Australia* is shipped to Britain.
5. Linen *from Ireland* is world famous.
6. Bulbs *from Holland* are of excellent quality.

EXERCISE 27

What is the language of the people of:

1. Spain? ....
2. Italy? ....
3. Sweden? ....
4. Denmark? ....
5. Russia? ....
6. Germany? ....
7. Norway? ....
8. Greece? ....
9. China? ....
10. Poland? ....

EXERCISE 28

Re-write the following sentences, using a shorter form in place of the words in italics:

1. The dog *belonging to Dick* is a collie.
2. Have you seen the pen *that belongs to Miss Smith?*

15

3. The hair *of the African* was long and curly.
4. The weapons *of the caveman* were made of bone.
5. The cattle *belonging to Farmer Green* broke out of the field.
6. The parrot *that Marie owns* is a splendid talker.

EXERCISE 29

Re-write the following, leaving out the words that are unnecessary:

1. The motor cycle was travelling fast as it quickly turned the corner.
2. The longer I live and the older I become, the more I learn.
3. Take a seat and sit down for you must be very tired.
4. Her work was all wrong and incorrect because she had been in such a hurry.
5. The carpenter nailed up the board with a hammer used for driving nails.
6. Leave that exercise in the meantime and we will soon come back to it again.

EXERCISE 30

Re-write the following, using capital letters, quotation marks and other punctuation marks where necessary:

1. when in london i visited westminster abbey
2. I entered my room picked up my bag and soon was off to newcastle
3. mothers first words were happy birthday
4. so this is your home exclaimed mervyn
5. I could not hear what he said could you
6. are you going im not

16

EXERCISE 31

Re-write the following, replacing the words in italics with those of opposite meaning:

1. The *old* footpath has a *rough* surface.
2. The *foolish* virgins carried *empty* lamps.
3. *Thin* men usually like *warm* weather.
4. To carry baby is *hard* work for a *small* boy.
5. The *large* car travelled *quickly down* the *long* hill.

EXERCISE 32

Fill in the blanks with a suitable " sound " word:

Example: A dog barks.

1. A bee ....
2. A cat ....
3. A cock ....
4. A pig ....
5. A sheep ....
6. A donkey ....
7. A horse ....
8. A pigeon. ....

EXERCISE 33

Opposite each of the following write its plural form:

Example: box, boxes.

1. cow, ...
2. sheep, ...
3. mouse, ...
4. fox, ...
5. calf, ...
6. goose, ...
7. donkey, ...
8. potato, ...
9. fly, ...
10. child, ...

EXERCISE 34

The following passage fits Yesterday. Write it to suit To-day:

" They fought the dogs and killed the cats,
And bit the babies in their cradles.
And ate the cheeses out of the vats,
And licked the soup from the cooks' own ladles."

Begin:
" They are fighting ...."

EXERCISE 35

Write the names of the instruments used for the following purposes:
1. To fix a screw.
2. To cut wood.
3. To take a photograph.
4. To darn a sock.
5. To pick up small pieces of iron.
6. To shave.
7. To find direction at sea or in the air.
8. To cut cloth.

EXERCISE 36

Fill in the blanks with suitable words:
1. We all sat as .... as mice.
2. The lazy fellow is as .... as a pig.
3. She is as .... as a mule.
4. In her new frock she was as .... as a peacock.
5. The soldier was as .... as a lion.
6. After the accident she was trembling like a ....
7. In the sunshine the calm sea shone like ....
8. The lake water is as clear as ....

EXERCISE 37

Here are eight names:
Hair, welcome, birds, elephant, clowns, bees, wolves, lawns.

Here are eight describing words:
Buzzing, green, hearty, wavy, warbling, funny, huge, fierce.

Choose a suitable describing word to go with each name and then use each pair of words in a sentence.

Name the person who does each of the following jobs:
1. Mends footwear.
2. Sells medicines, pills, etc.
3. Keeps the streets clean.
4. Directs the traffic at busy corners.
5. Repairs engines of cars.
6. Amuses people at a circus.
7. Keeps a building clean and looks after the fires, etc.
8. Sows the seed and harvests the crops.

EXERCISE 39

Fill in the blank spaces with the correct words taken from the brackets:
1. (To, too, two) pounds is (to, too, two) much (to, too, two) pay for that hat.
2. We (come, came) to the marsh (were, where) we (saw, seen) a flock of ducks flying north.
3. They (was, were) in a (great, grate) hurry.
4. Father and mother (has, have) (went, gone) for a (tour, tower) in a bus.
5. The wind (blue, blew) her (hair, hare) into her eyes.
6. (Them, those) books over (their, there) are mine.

EXERCISE 40

Complete the following to make sentences:
1. The little children were playing, when ....
2. They stood in the shed whilst ....
3. He ran so quickly that ....
4. Kindly put your books away before ....
5. The girl cannot sew because ....
6. I will come as soon as ....

EXERCISE 41

Complete the following to make sentences:
1. If .... give her my good wishes.
2. If .... I shall be glad to see you.
3. If .... we shall have a jolly time.
4. Though .... I did not go to bed.
5. Though .... he won the race easily.
6. Though .... he is nearly 1.80 metres in height.

EXERCISE 42

Write only the sentences from the following and underline the verb in each:
1. The mouse ran up the clock.
2. A lion sleeping in his den.
3. One a penny, two a penny, hot cross buns.
4. A hunter set a snare for the lion.
5. The cords torn by the sharp teeth of the mouse.
6. Monkeys chatter.
7. Do your work neatly.

EXERCISE 43

Put in capital letters, quotation marks, apostrophes and other punctuation marks:
1. whats that noise
2. we had cakes bread and butter jam and honey for tea
3. what a jolly game
4. yes he said the water was quite warm
5. good-bye he shouted I ll see you next friday
6. my goodness he exclaimed its toms dog rover

EXERCISE 44

Write sentences in answer to the following:

1. It is now getting on for mid-day; what hour did the clock last strike?
2. If a man is close upon fifty years, is he more or less than fifty?
3. Tim was asked to play football. He refused point-blank. What did he say?
4. At the party, there were thirty present at the outside. How many might have been there?

EXERCISE 45

Join each of the following pairs of sentences to make one sentence:

1. I shall play in the match. It takes place on Saturday.
2. My friend did not win the first prize. He was not feeling fit.
3. She fell into the river. She was watching the boat race.
4. The workman was careless. The work had to be done again.
5. The lady screamed. The robber disappeared.
6. We dressed in our best clothes. Grandma was coming to see us.

EXERCISE 46

Write the following sentences in a different order so as to make a well-arranged story, beginning with the second sentence:

The donkey, however, resisted with all his might and the driver, in disgust, let go his hold. A donkey which was being driven along a road near the sea left the beaten

21

track and made off for the cliffs. Thereupon the animal plunged to his death. Just as he was about to fall over the driver seized him by the tail and tried to pull him back.
Give your story a suitable title.

EXERCISE 47

Re-arrange the following sentences to make a continued story:

He tried in vain to find the path and then, tired and despairing, he sat down and cried. When he decided he would have to spend the night on the cold, damp hills, a voice hailed him and in a few moments his father was by his side. Fog rose from the valley and spread quickly over the hills so that he was unable to find his way home. Michael was sent out on the hills to look after his father's sheep. Everything seemed strange in the gloom.

EXERCISE 48

Fill in " past " or " passed " in the following:
1. Many famous battles have been fought in the
   ....
2. The circus .... along our street.
3. We have tea at half .... five.
4. Jill .... from fourth class to fifth class.
5. How many cars have .... during the .... five minutes?
6. The weather has been unsettled during the .... few days.
7. In the .... soldiers wore armour in battle.
8. He .... the chair through the window.

EXERCISE 49

Fill in " may " or " can " in the following:

1. .... I have my lunch now?
2. .... a young duck swim?
3. The weight-lifter .... raise that huge weight.
4. .... I leave the room, please?
5. Mother said, " You .... go if you wish."
6. This .... be true but I do not think it .... be.
7. The boy .... vault that fence.
8. Those who have tickets .... come in.

EXERCISE 50

Complete the following to make more interesting sentences:

1. The rain was ....
2. The boys were playing ....
3. He has the book which ....
4. The lady spoke when ....
5. The door was banging ....
6. They were running ....
7. The shop was blazing ....
8. We were joking ....

EXERCISE 51

Put the following sentences in their proper order to make a good paragraph, leaving out the sentence that does not form part of the story:

1. The boy was nicknamed " Grump " because he was always grumbling. The master ordered his servant to leave the room. In a shabby little house on the edge of the town, lived a young boy and his mother. His mother had had many troubles in her life-time.

23

2. He was about to cross Main Street when he jumped on hearing a loud crash. Joe did well in his English test that morning. The lorry and the bus were both badly damaged. A lorry had just turned the corner from North Street and crashed into a bus.
3. One afternoon Jack was sailing his boat down the river. It caught in the branches of an overhanging tree. He had had a good dinner that day. The branch bent under his weight and he slipped off into the water. He could not reach it from the bank so he climbed out on one of the branches to set his boat free. Fortunately the water was not very deep and he was able to scramble out but he was soaking and had to run home very quickly to get dry clothing.

EXERCISE 52

From the following paragraph, write <u>ten</u> words that are the names of things and then write <u>seven</u> words that describe the things in your first list:

" Then there was the garden to see, and a most beautiful garden it was: long and narrow, with a straight, gravel walk down the middle of it; and at the end a green arbour with a bench under it. There were rows of cabbages and radishes, and peas and beans. I was delighted to see them, for I had never seen so much as a cabbage growing before."

EXERCISE 53

The following story was told by Ellen. Tell it in the form of a letter written by Maisie to her chum, Gwen. Use your own address as a heading and write as the first sentence of your letter, " I promised to tell you about my

party." **Maisie would probably say at the close of her letter that she was very sorry that Gwen could not attend her party.**

"It was Maisie's birthday yesterday. Her mother baked her a beautiful cake and put ten candles on it. How old do you think Maisie is now? There were six of us invited to the party. We played a great many games and I won a book in a Quiz."

EXERCISE 54

From the following paragraph, write the words that tell of doing something (9), verbs, and then write the names of people or things mentioned (10), nouns:

The children ran and shouted on the sands. The old ladies sat and chatted while they knitted. Two men pushed a boat into the water, climbed into it and rowed about. Later the pierrots gave a performance to a large crowd of interested young people.

EXERCISE 55

If you think any of the following are silly or not clear in meaning, re-write them so that they are sensible:

1. My boy is suffering from eyesight.
2. In the air crash only two lives were fortunately lost.
3. You're telling untrue lies.
4. He shot himself after writing a letter to his wife with a pistol.
5. I drove to the hotel where I had dinner in my car.
6. A tiger was shot by a man, measuring two metres from the nose to the tip of the tail.
7. Here lies James Jones who came here for the good of his health and died in 1949.
8. An umbrella was lost by a woman with a curiously-shaped head.

EXERCISE 56

Write sentences saying why you should not do any of the following things:
1. Enter a room without knocking.
2. Close the door with a bang.
3. Play games on the street.
4. Throw orange peel on the footpath.
5. Sit on damp grass.
6. Often stay up late at night.

EXERCISE 57

Write eight lines to describe the scene which the following phrases and sentences bring to your mind:

Crowd of children at play; happy shouts; laughter; bell rings; whistle blows; children silent; "Fall in!"

EXERCISE 58

Read the following sentences, and then continue the story:

A little boy was about to run across the street, when his sister saw a motor-cycle coming quickly along. She shouted to him ....

EXERCISE 59

Write out the following, beginning with the words: "Joan's rabbits" and changing all other words where necessary:

Joan's rabbit escaped from its hutch one morning, and the little girl was greatly worried about it. She searched for it in the garden; in the shed; and in the greenhouse, but could not catch a glimpse of its little white tail

26

anywhere. Then she heard Prince barking near the wood pile. She ran to it, peeped amongst the wood, and there she saw her pet. It was trying to get further into the pile, away from the dog.

EXERCISE 60

Re-write the following paragraph, beginning with: " He saw a light " and changing other words where necessary:

I see a light flashing at the end of the road, and run towards it. When I get nearer, I go more slowly because I am rather timid, and I do not know what it really means. I laugh at myself when I find that it is only a little boy, reflecting the lamplight with a piece of broken mirror.

EXERCISE 61

Use each of the following groups of words in sentences:

1. days, shorter, begin, autumn, grow.
2. Jane, sister, aeroplane, first, yesterday.
3. school, enjoy, reading, story books, interesting.
4. farmer, boy, chased, angry, orchard.
5. fishing, hours, man, caught, trout.
6. lightning, torrent, skin, rumbling, soaked.

EXERCISE 62

Complete each of the following to make sentences:
1. Running down the road, he ....
2. Listening to the wireless, father ....

27

3. Dashing through the gate, the girl ....
4. Glancing out of the window, I ....
5. Seeing a snake in the grass, the traveller ....
6. Going to the door, Meta ....
7. Taking some money from his pocket, the gentleman ....
8. Swinging from branch to branch, the monkey ....

EXERCISE 63

Put in apostrophes where necessary:
1. One of the girls saw the girls hat.
2. A few of the boys ran to pick up the boys bicycle.
3. The suns rays are very bright.
4. Their countrys soldiers were gallant fellows.
5. The towns streets were badly lighted.
6. In a weeks time we shall be going away.
7. The tramps boots were tied with string.
8. They remembered their nations heroes.

EXERCISE 64

Complete the following, using the correct word taken from the brackets:
1. She plays very (good, well).
2. The policeman told him to drive (slow, slowly).
3. That drawing is (surely, sure) the best!
4. The angry dog barked (fiercely, fierce).
5. He had (near, nearly) finished his homework.
6. Come (quick, quickly).
7. The old lady spoke very (quiet, quietly).
8. He patted the sick puppy very (gently, gentle).

28

EXERCISE 65

Make sentences using each of the following words in two ways:

Example: nail.—The nail was rusty.
The carpenter nailed the board to the wall.

1. watch   (*a*) .... (*b*) ....
2. bark.   (*a*) .... (*b*) ....
3. hammer. (*a*) .... (*b*) ....
4. ring.   (*a*) .... (*b*) ....
5. rule.   (*a*) .... (*b*) ....
6. order. (*a*) .... (*b*) ....
7. reply. (*a*) .... (*b*) ....
8. act.   (*a*) .... (*b*) ....

EXERCISE 66

Combine each of the following pairs of sentences, using " who," " whom," " whose," " which " or " that ":

1. This is the path. It leads to the cave.
2. That is the girl. She won the prize.
3. He bought the book. You told him to read it.
4. My sister found the ball. It was lost.
5. The man is my friend. You met him.
6. We live in this cottage. My grandfather built it.
7. I read the book. It was given to me by my auntie.
8. There is the farmer. His horse ran off.

EXERCISE 67

Fill in capital letters, quotation marks, commas and other punctuation marks:

1. This is where you wanted off said the conductor
2. Hurry and bring me the answers said the teacher
3. The crowd shouted long live the president
4. We had a delightful meal replied the girls

5. The sailor remarked this is not very good sailing weather.
6. The lion called all the animals together and said we must have a discussion
7. If you follow this road you will come to the castle said the policeman
8. Now for the fire-works said Bill

EXERCISE 68

Write the questions for which the following are answers:

1. The car was put in the garage.
2. The book belongs to Miss Gordon.
3. Yes, you may go when you have completed your work.
4. " Good-bye " means " God be with you."
5. King Alfred the Great founded the British Navy.
6. Saint Francis of Assisi was supposed to have preached to the birds.
7. Holly leaves are prickly to prevent animals from eating them.
8. Lawn tennis was first played about 1870.

EXERCISE 69

Put quotation marks round the actual words of the speaker:

1. The troop-leader said come as early as you can.
2. Ella's mother said send me a cable as soon as you arrive.
3. It is very cold said mother.
4. I will help you to count them said Bob.
5. Are you sure you saw her said the policeman.
6. He arrived late said the servant to me.
7. What a mess said nurse.
8. I will ring the gong when tea is ready said Jane.

EXERCISE 70

Look at the five sentences below; they are supposed to tell what Jack did last Saturday. One of the sentences should be left out. Two of the sentences should be joined by " but," and the other two by " and." Re-write the description properly:

Jack has a puppy called Bones. Jack went to visit his cousin James last Saturday. Jack rose early on Saturday morning. Jack and James played football at first. When they grew tired of this they played at cowboys and Indians.

EXERCISE 71

Fill in the blank spaces with words from the brackets:
1. Desmond (through, threw) a stone (through, threw) the window.
2. Edward has a (pane, pain) in his arm.
3. The traveller (told, tolled) many strange (tails, tales).
4. " Of (course, coarse)," she said, " you must use (course, coarse) thread."
5. After I have bought some (meet, meat) I shall (meet, meat) you at the Post Office.
6. The boat with the red (sail, sale) was for (sail, sale).
7. The child was (to, too, two) young (to, too, two) learn algebra.
8. He (rode, road) on horseback down the (rode, road).

EXERCISE 72

Fill in the blank spaces with words from the brackets:
1. Her coat is (wore, worn) out.
2. The child was (bit, bitten, bite) by the vicious dog.

3. The choir (sang, sung) a beautiful song.
4. The cat (sprang, sprung) on the bird.
5. The injured man was (took, taken) to the hospital.
6. Father had (rose, risen) early to catch the train.
7. The tramp's clothing was badly (tore, torn).
8. The bell was (rang, rung) at one o'clock.

EXERCISE 73

Complete the following to make sentences:

1. .... is the season when the birds build their nests.
2. .... is the season of hail and frost.
3. .... helps her mother to wash the dishes.
4. .... caught a rat.
5. .... wrote a letter to his uncle.
6. .... roam the countryside.
7. .... burns brightly.
8. .... live in countries near the Arctic Circle.

EXERCISE 74

Fill in the blank spaces with the correct form of the word in brackets:

1. The girls .... as fast as they could.   (run.)
2. Jill .... the lions at the zoo.   (see.)
3. He .... on that seat yesterday.   (sit.)
4. The aircraft .... in formation across the sky.   (fly.)
5. The little boy .... all the sweets.   (eat.)
6. The wind .... fiercely during the night.   (blow.)
7. Nan .... a letter to her friend.   (write.)
8. The parcel .... yesterday.   (come.)
9. She .... to the shop for her mother.   (go.)
10. He .... all his work in good time.   (do.)

EXERCISE 75

Fill in the blanks with the correct words from the brackets:

1. The (carpenter, bricklayer, slater) broke his (saw, hammer, patient) when he (cut, drove, read) the timber.
2. The (traveller, butler, doctor) visited his (book, servant, patient) every (year, month, day) last week.
3. A (flock, herd, swarm) of cattle and a (herd, flock, swarm) of sheep were grazing in the field.
4. The (church, house, shop) was built as a (factory, school, residence) for the (teacher, minister, manager) of the bank.

EXERCISE 76

Put each of the following answers in the form of questions:

1. " There are no giants now," said John.
    - (*a*) Who ....?
    - (*b*) What ....?
    - (*c*) What ....?
2. " I think that we need another assistant," said Mrs. Adams to her husband one day at dinner.
    - (*a*) What ....?
    - (*b*) To whom ....?
    - (*c*) When ....?
3. The king waited to see who would prove the best soldiers.
    - (*a*) Who ....?
    - (*b*) What ....?
    - (*c*) Why ....?
4. First she took a pencil and diary and wrote down each thing she would do.
    - (*a*) What ....?
    - (*b*) How ....?
    - (*c*) Why ....?

5. The two companies of soldiers that went to slay the dragon were killed.
   (*a*) What ....?
   (*b*) How ....?
   (*c*) What happened ....?

EXERCISE 77

Write down words having the <u>opposite</u> meaning to the following:

1. sour, ...	7. heavy, ...
2. swift, ...	8. stout, ...
3. bright, ...	9. deep, ...
4. calm, ...	10. this, ...
5. foe, ...	11. small, ...
6. these, ...	12. tall, ...

Use some of the words you found above, to fill the blank spaces in the following:

1. We enjoyed the ...., Canadian apples.
2. The ...., starved prisoners ate their food ravenously.
3. Though the parcel was large it was ....
4. The small children were wading in the .... water.
5. The little ship was driven on the rocks in the .... seas.
6. The funeral approached at a .... pace.
7. As the afternoon was very hot, I bought a .... ice.
8. A .... in need is a .... indeed.

EXERCISE 78

Re-write the following sentences, putting in capitals and punctuation marks:

1. be careful where you are walking said jim as tom drew near

34

2. if i were you id build a truck for myself said jimmy
3. are you going to marys party on tuesday next asked irene
4. said big chief lynx-eye bring the palefaces to me
5. yes it would be quite easy said blackbeard
6. cant you manage it milly asked elsie

EXERCISE 79

There are different ways of expressing the same thought. From the following groups of sentences, write out the two that tell the same thought:

1. I do not like to play hockey. Hockey is a game I dislike. I have never played hockey.
2. The glove is too small for your hand. Your hand is too small for the glove. The glove is too large for you.
3. It is a fine day. The weather is improved. We are having glorious weather to-day.
4. A dog has four legs. If it has four legs it is a dog. There are four legs on a dog.
5. I am not very anxious to go. I would almost as soon stay. I would rather go.

EXERCISE 80

In two other ways write the same thought as is contained in the following:

1. The bus was late because of the heavy storm.
   (*a*) .... (*b*) ....
2. Tuesday and Wednesday are the two days on which we have geography.
   (*a*) .... (*b*) ....
3. It is dangerous to cross the street without looking both ways.
   (*a*) .... (*b*) ....

4. There are many ways of catching a rabbit.
   (*a*) .... (*b*) ....

5. Margaret sat beside Doreen and June sat beside Margaret.
   (*a*) .... (*b*) ....

6. How can I go from this platform to that platform?
   (*a*) .... (*b*) ....

EXERCISE 81

Add phrases beginning with " in," " into," " of," " on," " down " or " with " to fill the blanks.

Example: The pen (on the desk) belongs to the girl (in our class).

1. The trees .... were covered ....
2. The thunder .... frightened the girls ....
3. The lady .... spoke to the children ....
4. The duchess .... drove through the streets ....
5. The pictures .... were painted ....
6. The terrier .... barked at the tramp ....
7. The chatter .... was heard by the boys ....
8. The soldiers .... paraded ....

EXERCISE 82

After each of the following words write the word of opposite meaning:

Examples: true, untrue; possible, impossible.

1. usual, ...
2. patient, ...
3. easy, ...
4. pure, ...
5. fair, ...
6. like, ...
7. perfect, ...
8. selfish, ...
9. proper, ...
10. comfortable, ...

EXERCISE 83

Use some of the words you found in the last exercise to fill the blank spaces.

1. You would do better work if you were not so ....
2. To drink .... water is very dangerous.
3. The high wooden bench was a most .... seat.
4. It was very .... of you to share your sweets with Doris.
5. It was .... Billy to miss a football match.
6. Mother began to feel .... when the children did not appear.
7. Though her work was ...., teacher was pleased that she had tried hard.
8. It was .... of Michael to copy from Jimmy's exercise.

EXERCISE 84

Fill in the blank spaces with " who," " which " or " that."

1. The boy .... ran so well in the race is my friend.
2. The thief stole the cow .... won first prize at the Show.
3. The old man .... lived here so long has gone away.
4. .... of the books would you like?
5. The hotel in .... we stayed belongs to my uncle.
6. The girl .... is sitting beside Meg is a skilful needleworker.

EXERCISE 85

The same sentence may often be read in different ways. If a person wishes to draw attention particularly to one part of the sentence, he emphasises that part.

Example: To say—" *Marie* gained the prize," means that Marie alone gained the prize.

To say—" Marie *gained* the prize," means that she obtained the prize in this particular way.

To say—" Marie gained the *prize*," means that this is what, in fact, she gained.

" *Marie* gained the prize " answers the question " *Who* gained the prize?"

" Marie *gained* the prize " answers the question "*How* did Marie obtain the prize?"

"Marie gained the *prize*" answers the question "*What* did Marie gain?"

Write suitable questions for which the following are answers:

1. They went home by bus *after the concert.*
2. Jane went *to auntie's* yesterday.
3. The train had just arrived *from Glasgow.*
4. *I* told them the story.
5. Harry went to the game *with his father.*
6. Belfast is the capital of *Northern Ireland.*
7. *No,* Alfred is *not* our champion jumper.
8. *Gordon* will be able to go, but *Kathryn* will not.
9. Australia produces *wool and mutton.*
10. The road is *up-hill* from Greystones to Yew Villa.

EXERCISE 86

Combine the following pairs of sentences by replacing the words in italics with a suitable " joining " word:

1. I saw the man. *The man* was a champion boxer.
2. He damaged the bicycle. *The bicycle* belonged to his father.
3. I went with Florence to the theatre. I met *Florence* at the bus terminus.

4. John is nearly eleven years old. *John* is learning Latin.
5. Jill made an omelette for tea. *The omelette* was very appetising.
6. The teacher read two stories on Thursday. *The stories* were most interesting.
7. I found Mary's gym shoes. I gave the *gym shoes* to Mary.
8. Susan bought two bars of chocolate. She gave *the two bars of chocolate* to her brother.

EXERCISE 87

Write out the names used for each of the following:

1. a young cat, ...
5. a young hen, ...
2. a young dog, ...
6. a young sheep, ...
3. a young duck, ...
7. a young horse, ...
4. a young goose, ...
8. a young bird, ...

EXERCISE 88

Fill in the blank spaces with words made from those in brackets:

1. Father had to .... my load so that I could climb the hill. (light.)
2. " This space must be .... to make two hockey pitches," said the man. (large.)
3. The .... of the path was not great enough so the workmen had to .... it by one metre. (wide.)
4. They were greatly .... when wealthy uncle Harry died and left them all his money. (rich.)
5. The artist did some .... work in his studio. (beauty.)

39

EXERCISE 89

Fill in the blank spaces with suitable words:

1. Billy fell .... the pony.
2. They .... to the .... of the mountain.
3. Father .... a cine camera .... me.
4. The bold robber .... the bank is daylight.
5. She put her hat .... her ....
6. The sweets .... divided .... the three of us.
7. We strolled .... the field.
8. The notice in the bus read: " Please keep your .... the seat in front."
9. On the way to .... I sat .... my friend.
10. The express .... through the little station.

EXERCISE 90

Complete the following sentences using one word for the words in brackets:

1. The car (that belongs to the doctor) ....
2. The shop (that belongs to Mr. Brown) ....
3. The tail (that belongs to our cat) ....
4. The rudder (of the ship) ....
5. The song (of the lark) ....
6. The rays (of the sun) ....

EXERCISE 91

Re-write the following sentences in the plural form:

Example: The girl was wearing her blazer.
The girls were wearing their blazers.

1. The attache case has a leather handle.
2. The puppy was chasing his tail.
3. The cottage belongs to my friend.
4. The river flows under the bridge.
5. The woman loves her pet.

6. The mouse was caught in the trap.
7. The goose was being fattened for Christmas.
8. Here comes the man and his wife.

EXERCISE 92

Fill in the blank spaces with the proper word from the brackets:

1. The lady .... a song. The song was .... (sung, sang.)
2. The men .... the work. The work was .... (did, done.)
3. I .... the Exhibition. We have .... the Exhibition. (seen, saw.)
4. I will .... you to swim. You will .... to swim. (learn, teach.)
5. .... are my football boots. I bought .... in town. (those, them.)
6. It was .... who did it. Will you play with Bill and ....? (me, I.)
7. The .... girl does her work .... (well, good.)
8. .... I borrow your book? I .... read quickly. (may, can.)

EXERCISE 93

Re-write the following sentences correctly:

1. I don't know nothing about it.
2. I haven't got none of them.
3. Your father forbade you not to go.
4. I didn't have no lunch.
5. I want for to go too.
6. After taking the medicine, he did not feel no better.
7. He said he would not do it no more.
8. She did not do no practising to-day.

41

EXERCISE 94

Fill in the blanks with suitable words:

1. The .... man slept .... in his bed.
2. The .... boys rushed .... into the play-ground.
3. The .... bird .... a merry song in the trees.
4. The .... children ran .... home to tell the news.
5. The .... boy listened .... to the old man's story.
6. We ate a .... breakfast and .... for school.

EXERCISE 95

John told the following story a few days ago. Tell the story as Peter would tell it to-day:

Peter and I are going to explore in the mountains to-morrow. I shall call for Peter at ten o'clock in the morning and we shall take the bus to Newcastle. I am taking the eatables and Peter will supply fruit and something to drink. We hope the weather will be fine and that we shall have an enjoyable time. We expect to be home in time for supper.

EXERCISE 96

" Nice " is a word often used incorrectly. In the following replace the word " nice " with a more expressive word:

Example: a nice pie; a delicious pie.

1. a nice day, ...
2. a nice man, ...
3. a nice dress, ...
4. a nice house, ...
5. a nice town, ...
6. nice hair, ...
7. nice flowers, ...
8. nice manners, ...

42

EXERCISE 97

Fill in the blank spaces with suitable " action " words:

1. The lamp-lighter .... the lamps.
2. The shoemaker .... the shoes.
3. The dress-maker .... the seam.
4. The moon .... between the clouds.
5. The sun .... over the eastern horizon.
6. The dog .... the rabbit.
7. The ducks .... across the pond.
8. The mouse .... the cheese.

EXERCISE 98

Fill in the blanks with suitable words taken from the following list:

Words: patiently, carefully, noisily, loudly, gently,
faithfully, merrily, soundly.

1. In his steel-toed boots the miner walked very
....
2. The watchdog barked ....
3. The boy waited .... for his father.
4. In spite of the storm, baby slept ....
5. I lifted the injured bird ....
6. The thoughtful girl does her lessons ....
7. The old servant always did his duty ....
8. The happy children sang ....

EXERCISE 99

Combine the following pairs of sentences using the following " joining " words: " as," " after," " where " or " because ":

1. The birds flew away.   The noisy children approached.
2. The boys returned home.   The game was over.

3. The sun shone brilliantly. The thunder-storm had passed.
4. Mary was top of her class. She always worked very hard.
5. The bridge was built. The river was narrow at that point.
6. The young horse ran away. The road-roller frightened him.
7. There boys liked to play. Woods and caves were there.
8. The bells pealed merrily. The girls were passing.

EXERCISE 100

Re-write the following sentences using words of opposite meaning to those in italics:

1. I am *glad* that you were *early*.
2. *She* is a very *strong* girl.
3. The *little* dog has a *short* tail.
4. The apples were *hard* and *sour*.
5. The *young* lady went through the *broad* door.
6. My *brother* is wearing an *old* coat.
7. The *lazy* boy arrived *late* at school.
8. The *speedy* runner was *first* in the race.

SUBJECTS FOR COMPOSITION EXERCISES

1. I am a bus driver . . .
2. If I could become invisible for a day.
3. A country I should like to visit.
4. A tramp.
5. Our milkman.
6. How to sew on a button.
7. How to set and light a fire.
8. Seen from the hill-top.
9. The view from my bedroom window.
10. A house on fire.
11. A narrow escape. A story told by a mouse.
12. Fairyland.
13. A gipsy's life.
14. Fun on the beach on a fine summer afternoon.
15. Heavy rain . . . flooding.
16. A Christmas tree tells its story.
17. The loveliest month.
18. Lost in the woods.
19. Describe a bird's nest you found.
20. Harvesting.
21. A snowball fight.
22. Market day in a country town. (A busy scene in the city.)
23. A former school-friend has written to you from Australia, asking for news of schoolmates. Write your reply.
24. The present I should like to receive next birthday.
25. Helping the old lady down the street.
26. I am a swallow . . .
27. Chased by an angry bull.
28. The queer old man in the end house.
29. At that moment the lantern went out.
30. My purse was gone!
31. The clock struck midnight. I heard a scratching sound . . .
32. A swing . . . looking over the branches . . . Snap!

33. If I had an aeroplane.

34. Taking care of my teeth.

35. When I was ill.

36. The tits help themselves to our milk.

37. The day we break-up for summer holidays.

38. The scarecrow tells his story.

39. A new pair of roller skates or an air-gun.

40. A wish.

41. Buying a new coat.

42. A great surprise.

43. It was the most difficult thing I ever tried to do.

44. Saving for a new bicycle or a holiday.

45. Some day I'll go there.

46. My hobby.

47. The game I am most fond of or a pleasant occupation.

48. A play you enjoyed or in which you had a part.

49. The person in history I should like to have known.

50. I wish I could change places with him for a day.

51. A journey by aeroplane, bus or boat.

52. Write a letter inviting a friend to your Hallowe'en party. Your friend's reply.

53. Write a letter from your mother to the Principal of your school apologising for your absence last Friday.

54. Write a letter to your auntie (or uncle) thanking her for the present sent to you on your birthday.

55. A very important person you know.

56. The chimney sweep.

57. An old, broken-down lorry tells its story.

58. I treasure it more than any other possession.

59. Write a letter to a friend telling him or her of a very interesting book you have had on loan from the library and saying why you enjoyed it.

60. Write a letter to a friend in hospital, giving him or her the news of interest and expressing hopes for his or her quick recovery.

61. You are camping (or spending a holiday with a country friend). Write home to tell your mother how you are enjoying yourself and stating when you expect to return home.

62. A conversation between two women in a queue outside a bakery (or between two men in a queue outside a football ground).

63. Going on an errand on a dark night.

64. Suppose you are a detective. Tell how you caught a thief.

65. I made it myself. Describe the article and how you did the work.

66. An evening at a party.

67. An old umbrella relates an adventure.

68. A fight between two dogs.

69. "Just wait till I get my hands on you!" shouted the angry owner. Tell about the events which led up to this outburst.

70. How to make a kite (or how to prepare a poached egg).

71. A brave deed.

72. Looking after baby.

73. The best present I ever received.

74. What I like to read.

75. Tell about what you are fond of collecting.

76. If I were a rich man.

77. A visitor came to our town and wrote a letter in which he said what he thought of it. Write the letter.

78. Shop windows.

79. The station on a busy afternoon.

80. If I had a Magic Carpet.